Let's Read!

Read the Page

Read the Story

Game

Sound It / Say It

Repeat

Stop

Get-Ready Words

animals	mountain
castle	rainbow
enchanted	riddle
forest	squirrel
message	unicorn

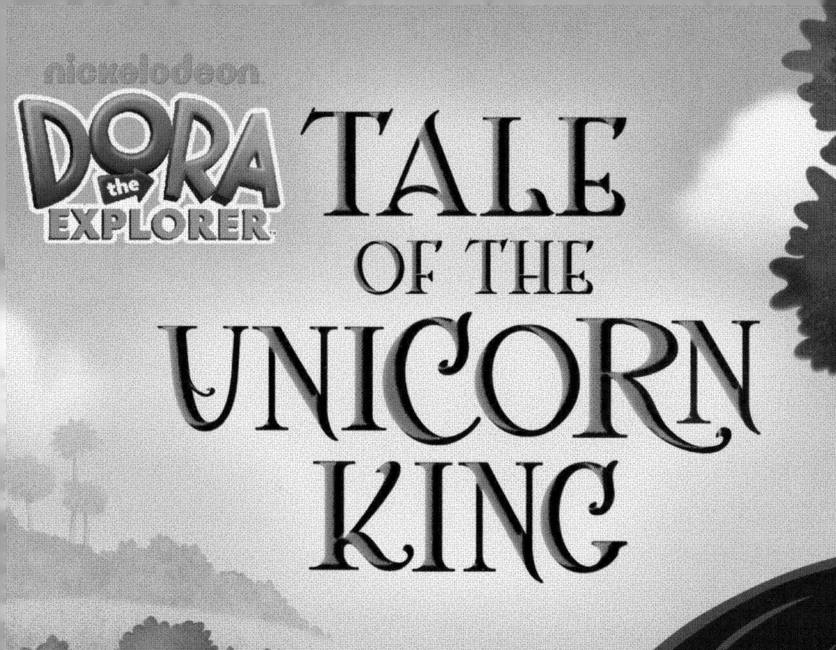

TALE OF THE UNICORN KING

Based on the screenplay "King Unicornio"
written by Rosemary Contreras
Illustrated by Victoria Miller

Hi! I am Dora. This is Boots.
It is spring. Do you see a rainbow?

Our friend Unicornio is coming down the rainbow. Unicornio is a unicorn. He's the best!

Look! There is a rabbit.
What did she bring?

The rabbit has a message for Unicornio. The animals of the Enchanted Forest want Unicornio to be their king.

Hooray, Unicornio!

A king must be kind, smart, brave and strong. Unicornio is not sure he is all of those things. We will help show him he can be a king.

We will help you, Unicornio.
We will all go on a quest to
find the Enchanted Castle
and get Unicornio's crown.

How do we find the castle?

Let's ask Map!

First, we need to go through the Riddle Tree.

Then, we go past Dragon Mountain.

That is how we get to the Enchanted Castle.

Look! There is a tiny elf. He is too small to reach the fruit in the tall tree.

Unicornio can help! Unicornio is kind, just like a king needs to be.

We found the Riddle Tree.
The Riddle Tree will let us
through if we answer a riddle.

Unicornio can answer the riddle!
Unicornio is smart, just like a
king needs to be.

We made it to Dragon Mountain.

That did not take long. Great!

Oh no! There is a dragon!

Unicornio needs to use his magic to protect us from the dragon.

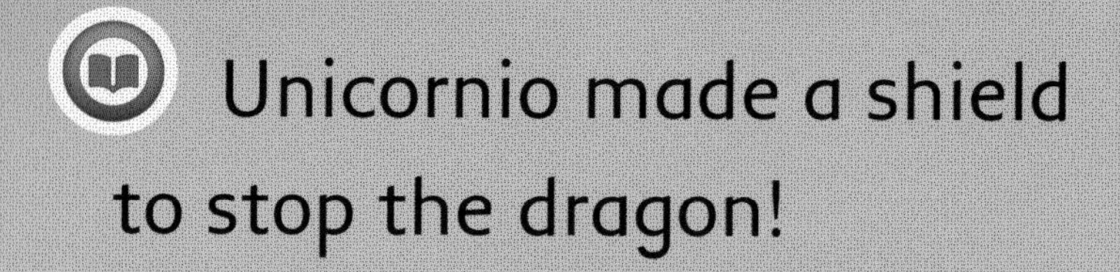

Unicornio made a shield
to stop the dragon!

Unicornio is brave, just like a king needs to be.

We are almost at the castle. Oh, no! A brown squirrel needs help, and fast!

I bet Unicornio can pull
the squirrel to safety.

Unicornio saved the squirrel! Unicornio is strong, just like a king needs to be.

The rabbit gives Unicornio a crown. The animals were not wrong. Unicornio is kind, smart, brave, and strong. He is a true king!

The End

Words You're Learning

Short Vowels

Short a Words	Short e Words	Short i Words	Short o Words	Short u Words
ask	best	did	on	just
can	elf	him	not	must
fast	help	his	stop	us
map		will		
past				

Long Vowels

Long a Words	Long e Words	Long i Words	Long o Words	Long u/oo Words
brave	be	hi	go	fruit
made	he	like	no	too
take	need		show	true
	see			
	tree			

Word Families

-all Words	-et Words	-ing Words	-ong Words	-own Words
all	bet	bring	long	brown
small	get	king	strong	crown
tall	let	spring	wrong	down

Sight Words

a	for	in	use
and	has	is	were
are	how	it	want
at	I	of	what
do	if	the	you